IFIELD COMMUNITY COLLEGE

Books are to be returned on or before the last date below

Ransom Neutron Stars
The Lottery Ticket
by Cath Jones
Illustrated by Morgan Swofford

Published by Ransom Publishing Ltd.
Unit 7, Brocklands Farm, West Meon, Hampshire GU32 1JN, UK
www.ransom.co.uk

ISBN   978 178591 442 3
First published in 2017
Reprinted 2018

The Lottery Ticket

Cath Jones

Illustrated by Morgan Swofford

Ransom

Ali was in a shop with Salma.

"Let's get a ticket for the lottery,"
Ali said. "I've got a pound coin."

They got a lottery ticket
with Ali's pound coin.

"I hope we win," Salma said.

"Me too!" Ali said.

Ali had on a red top. It had a big pocket.

He put the ticket in his pocket.

Ali and Salma got in the car
and went home.

"Let's watch TV," Ali said.

They looked at the lottery on TV.

"Did we win?" Salma said.

Ali jumped up.

"Whoopee!" he said. "We won!"

"Are we rich?" Salma said.

"Yes," Ali said. "We're rich. How exciting!"

"Woo hoo! Rich!" Salma said. "Can I look at the ticket?"

Ali looked in his pocket.

The lottery ticket wasn't in his pocket!

"Do you have the ticket?" Ali said.

"No, you had the ticket," Salma said.

"It was in the pocket of the red top.

Have you lost the ticket, Ali?"

"No! It must be in the car," Ali said.

Ali got back in the car. He hunted
for the lottery ticket.
He didn't find it!

"Oh no!" Salma said. "We're not rich,
then."

"Let's go back to the shop," Ali said.

When they got back to the shop,
it was shut!

"Look," Ali said. "I can see the ticket
on the floor, inside the shop!"

Ali tapped on the shop door.

"Please open up!" he said.

A man came to the door.

"My lottery ticket is on the floor,"
Ali said.

The man gave them the ticket.

"Did you win?" said the man.

Ali nodded.

"We'll be rich!" Salma said.

Ali looked at the lottery ticket.

He checked the numbers.

Salma checked the numbers too.

Then the man checked the numbers
on the ticket.

"You did win," said the man. "But you aren't rich. You won ten pounds."

Ali and Salma spent the ten pounds

on fish and chips for tea!

Have you read?

Fit for Love

by Elizabeth Dale

In the Stars

by Alice Hemming

Have you read?

Planting My Garden

by Stephen Rickard

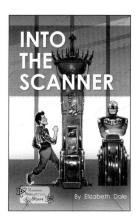

Into the Scanner

by Elizabeth Dale

Ransom Neutron Stars

The Lottery Ticket
Word count **318**

Yellow Book Band

Phonics

Phonics 1	Not Pop, Not Rock Go to the Laptop Man Gus and the Tin of Ham	*Phonics 2*	Deep in the Dark Woods Night Combat Ben's Jerk Chicken Van
Phonics 3	GBH Steel Pan Traffic Jam Platform 7	*Phonics 4*	The Rock Show Gaps in the Brain New Kinds of Energy

Book bands

Pink	Curry! Free Runners My Toys	*Red*	Shopping with Zombies Into the Scanner Planting My Garden
Yellow	Fit for Love **The Lottery Ticket** In the Stars	*Blue*	Awesome ATAs Wolves The Giant Jigsaw
Green	Fly, May FLY! How to Start Your Own Crazy Cult The Care Home	*Orange*	Text Me The Last Soldier Best Friends